Pooh's Activity Book

Draw more bees, so that there are 10 altogether, then colour your picture.

These pictures of Eeyore look the same,
but one is different.
Can you find and colour the odd one out?

3

Copy the picture of Rabbit square by square.
He's brown, with a white chest and tail.

4

These pictures of Owl look the same, but one is different. Can you find and colour the odd one out?

Rabbit   Eeyore   Piglet   Christopher Robin

These are some of Pooh's friends.
Draw lines to match their names and pictures.

Pooh and Christopher Robin are using a big umbrella as a boat.
Which jigsaw piece fits into the picture?

These pictures of Pooh look the same, but
one is different. Can you find and colour
the odd one out?

Look at the picture and tell the story
in your own words.

Can you help Piglet find the path that
leads to Pooh?

5   6   7   8   9   10

Count the butterflies and dragonflies,
and circle the right numbers.

11

Which of Pooh's friends is covered in snow?
Say his name, and draw more snowflakes to
complete the picture.

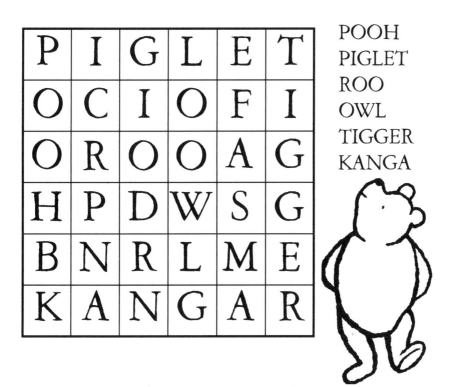

P	I	G	L	E	T
O	C	I	O	F	I
O	R	O	O	A	G
H	P	D	W	S	G
B	N	R	L	M	E
K	A	N	G	A	R

POOH
PIGLET
ROO
OWL
TIGGER
KANGA

Can you find the names of Pooh and some of
his friends in the word square?
The names are spelled out from side to side,
and from top to bottom.

13

Tigger loves playing with toys.
Colour the things you think he would like
to play with.

These 2 pictures look the same,
but there are 3 things that are different.
Can you find them all?

What a lot of honey, Pooh!
Count the jars, and write a number in the
box.

This is Kanga and her baby, Roo.
Can you tell the story in your own words?

Eeyore is a donkey, and he has lost his tail.
Can you find it for him, and draw it on?

Look at the pictures and
tell the story in your own words.

Piglet likes blowing dandelion seeds to make
them fly. Add a sun and some clouds to the
picture, then colour it as neatly as you can.

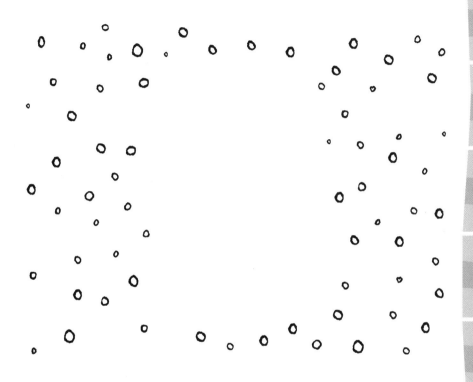

It's snowing again!
Draw a picture of Pooh in the snow.

Colour the picture of Eeyore and
his stick house as neatly as you can.

When Pooh gets stuck in a hole, he has to wait for his tummy to get smaller before he can get out. Christopher Robin reads to him to pass the time.

Can you find 3 things that are different in picture 2?

Colour this picture of Pooh and Piglet.